# Primary Mathematics
## Challenging Word Problems

**U.S. Edition**

Joseph D. Lee

Primary **4**

EPB PAN PACIFIC

## Panpac Education

Email: panpmktg@panpaceducation.com
Website: http://www.panpaceducation.com

EPB Pan Pacific is a trademark of Times Publishing Limited

ISBN 978-981-4208-83-3

First published 2004
Reprinted 2005
Reprinted 2006
Reprinted 2007

Distributed in the U.S.A. by SingaporeMath.com Inc

**SingaporeMath.com Inc**

*Printed by Utopia Press Pte Ltd*

*Printed in Singapore*

# Preface

**Primary Mathematics Challenging Word Problems** provides extra practice and challenge in solving word problems. It is written to complement the Primary Mathematics U.S. Edition textbooks and workbooks and follows the same sequence of topics.

The main objective of these books is to help the students improve their problem solving skills. To achieve this, a systematic coverage of most topics from the Primary Mathematics with their relevant exercises has been designed. The language used is simple and clear.

The books incorporate the following features:

*Topical Problems* — Each book is divided into units containing word problems pertaining to a particular topic.

*Review Problems* — Each book also includes one or more units of Review Problems that help the students to review and reinforce the skills acquired in the preceding topics.

*Answer Key* — Each book has an answer key at the end of the book for the student or the instructor to check the answers.

*Worked Examples* — Each unit of topical problems has three worked examples where the student is guided step by step towards solving the various types of word problems.

*Practice Problems* — Each unit and each set of review problems contain practice problems where the student can practice solving common word problems based on the topic.

*Challenging Problems* — The practice problems are followed by challenging word problems which require more thinking skills and creative problem solving strategies.

# How to use this book

- Read the worked examples and try to solve them on your own using a separate sheet of paper.

- Compare your solution to the given solution.

- If your answer is correct, congratulate yourself.

- If your solution is different, compare it to the given solution. A problem can have more than one good method of arriving at the same answer.

- If your answer is incorrect, try to understand where you went wrong.

- Then, try to solve the problems in the Practice Problems exercise.

- If you cannot solve one, do not give up. Think about it for a while. Try again later.

- When you have finished, check your answers by referring to the Answer Key.

- If you have an incorrect answer, find out where and why you have gone wrong. Ask for help if you need it.

- Next, try the problems in the Challenging Problems exercise.

- If you cannot solve some of the challenging problems, do not be disheartened or disappointed. They are more challenging than the usual word problems.

- After you have worked on a problem for a while and still cannot solve it, ask for help, and try to understand the solution. Then try to solve it on your own again later.

- The more you practice, the better you will get.

# Contents

# TOPICAL PROBLEMS 1

## WHOLE NUMBERS

### WORKED EXAMPLE 1

A customer can pay for a vacation with a deposit of $1480 and additional 9 monthly installments of $395 each. He can also make a one-time payment of $4850. How much more does it cost to pay by installments than by a one-time payment?

|  | $1480 | $395 |  |  |  |  |  |  |  | ? |
|---|---|---|---|---|---|---|---|---|---|---|
| Installments |  |  |  |  |  |  |  |  |  |  |

One-time payment — $4850

$9 \times 395 = 3555$

$1480 + 3555 = 5035$

It costs $5035 to pay by installments.

$5035 - 4850 = 185$

It costs **$185** more to pay by installments than by a one-time payment.

# WORKED EXAMPLE 2

Sam and Paul have 497 marbles altogether. If Sam has 59 marbles more than Paul, how many marbles does Sam have?

Sam

?

59

497

Paul

**If Paul has another 59 marbles...**

Sam

?

59

497 + 59

Paul

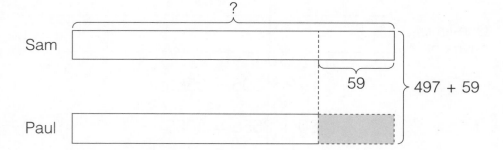

$$497 + 59 = 556$$

$$556 \div 2 = 278$$

Sam has **278** marbles.

## WORKED EXAMPLE 3

Linda had three times as many cookies as Hazel. After Linda ate 50 cookies, she had half as many cookies as Hazel. How many cookies did Linda have left?

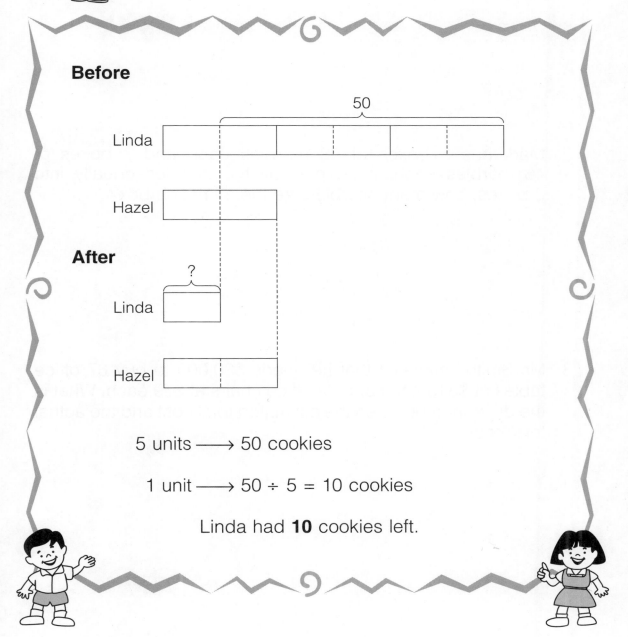

**Before**

50

Linda

Hazel

**After**

?

Linda

Hazel

5 units ⟶ 50 cookies

1 unit ⟶ 50 ÷ 5 = 10 cookies

Linda had **10** cookies left.

## Practice Problems

Solve each of these problems. Show your work and statements clearly.

1. Mr. Marshal needs $40,000 to employ 46 clerks and 4 cleaners each month. If he pays each clerk $820, how much does he pay each cleaner?

2. Mark has 3 boxes of 98 marbles each and 7 boxes of 46 marbles each. If he puts all the marbles equally into 8 boxes, how many marbles are there in each box?

3. Mr. Smith estimates that he needs $30,000 to buy 67 office tables at $318 each and 72 office chairs at $79 each. What is the difference between the estimated total cost and the actual total cost?

4. A man had 27 cartons of apples. Each carton contained 65 apples. He sold 184 apples on Monday and 213 apples on Tuesday. How many apples did he have left?

5. The table below shows Mr. Winston's monthly expenses. If he has a monthly income of $1420, how much does Mr. Winston save each month?

| Food | $178 |
|------|------|
| Rent | $420 |
| Transport | $84 |
| Others | $375 |

6. A grocer had 9 cartons of 143 oranges each. He sold 759 oranges and threw away 37 rotten ones. How many oranges did he have left?

7.  A man bought 7 cartons of shirts at $1152 per carton. There were 128 shirts in each carton. He sold each shirt for $25. How much money did he make altogether?

8.  Lucy had 48 pins. She had 17 fewer clips than pins. If she gave away 12 clips, how many pins and clips did she have left altogether?

9.  There are 15 sandwiches and 12 pieces of cake in a basket. Each sandwich weighs 89 g and each piece of cake weighs 54 g. If the basket weighs 317 g, find the total weight of the basket, sandwiches and cakes in grams.

10. James bought 4 boxes of marbles. Each box had 27 yellow marbles and 14 more red marbles than yellow marbles. If he lost 23 marbles, how many marbles did he have left?

11. There are 4 classes with 19 boys in each class and another 5 classes with 15 girls in each class. If there are 42 students in each of the 9 classes, how many girls are there altogether?

12. A man divided his fortune of $92,000 into 8 equal portions. He gave 4 portions to his wife, 1 portion to his son and shared the remaining portions equally among 5 charities. How much more money did his son get than each charity?

13. Shaun has 1483 stamps. Lily has 248 fewer stamps than Shaun. Calvin has 979 stamps more than Lily. How many more stamps does Calvin have than Shaun?

14. Mr. Robert bought 17 dozen belts. He sold 196 of them at $9 each. How much did he sell each of the remaining belts if the total amount collected from the sale of all the belts was $1860?

15. The total cost of 14 bags of rice, 25 bags of flour and 9 bags of beans is $1425. Each bag of rice costs $30 and each bag of flour costs $15. What is the cost of each bag of beans?

Solve each of these problems. Show your work and statements clearly.

16. May has 86 beads fewer than Sue. If they have 144 beads altogether, how many beads does May have?

17. Mr. Edward's monthly income is $3980. He spends $218 on food and three times as much on rent. He also spends $172 on clothing and half as much on transport. If he saves the rest of his income, what is his monthly savings?

18. A farmer had twice as many ducks as chickens. After he had sold 413 ducks and another 19 ducks died, he had half as many ducks as chickens left. How many ducks did he have left?

19. Laura and Helen have 207 beads altogether. Laura has 25 beads more than Helen. If Laura gives 18 of her beads to Helen, how many beads does Helen have in the end?

20. Jason had three times as many paper clips as Tim. After Jason gave 244 of his paper clips to Tim, he had the same number of paper clips as Tim. How many paper clips did they have altogether?

21. Vivian had 5 times as many stickers as Irene. After Vivian had given 20 of her stickers to Irene, she had twice as many stickers as Irene and 10 stickers more than Pam. How many stickers did Pam have?

22. Gina had three times as many strawberries as Fanny. After she had given 24 of her strawberries to Fanny, Gina had twice as many strawberries as Fanny. How many strawberries did they have altogether?

23. Ann and Clara had the same number of stickers. After Ann had given 48 of her stickers to Clara, Clara had 4 times as many stickers as Ann. How many stickers did Ann and Clara have altogether?

24. There are three times as many ducks as sheep on a farm. All the ducks and sheep have 2400 feet altogether. How many more ducks than sheep are there?

# TOPICAL PROBLEMS 2

# ADDITION AND SUBTRACTION OF FRACTIONS

## WORKED EXAMPLE 1

Mother bought a piece of cake. Janet ate $\frac{1}{10}$ of the cake and Sam ate $\frac{1}{5}$ of the cake. What fraction of the cake was left?

1

$\frac{1}{10}$  $\frac{1}{5}$  ?

$$\frac{1}{10} + \frac{1}{5} = \frac{1}{10} + \frac{2}{10}$$

$$= \frac{3}{10}$$

Janet and Sam ate $\frac{3}{10}$ of the cake altogether.

$$1 - \frac{3}{10} = \frac{10}{10} - \frac{3}{10}$$

$$= \frac{7}{10}$$

$\frac{7}{10}$ of the cake was left.

# WORKED EXAMPLE 2

Cindy has some stamps. $\frac{1}{4}$ of them are from Singapore, $\frac{1}{8}$ of them are from Japan and $\frac{3}{8}$ of them are from Hong Kong. The rest of them are from Malaysia. What fraction of her stamps are from Malaysia?

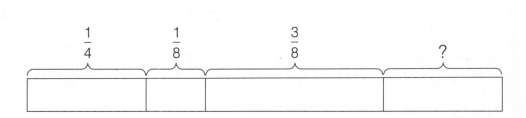

| $\frac{1}{4}$ | $\frac{1}{8}$ | $\frac{3}{8}$ | ? |

$$\frac{1}{4} + \frac{1}{8} + \frac{3}{8} = \frac{2}{8} + \frac{1}{8} + \frac{3}{8}$$

$$= \frac{6}{8}$$

$$= \frac{3}{4}$$

$$1 - \frac{3}{4} = \frac{4}{4} - \frac{3}{4}$$

$$= \frac{1}{4}$$

$\frac{1}{4}$ of her stamps are from Malaysia.

## WORKED EXAMPLE 3

Jack took $\frac{1}{3}$ h to solve a problem. Jimmy took $\frac{1}{6}$ h less than Jack to solve the same problem. Find the total time they took to solve the problem.

$\frac{1}{3}$ h

Jack

$\frac{1}{6}$ h

?

Jimmy

$$\frac{1}{3} - \frac{1}{6} = \frac{2}{6} - \frac{1}{6}$$

$$= \frac{1}{6}$$

Jimmy took $\frac{1}{6}$ h to solve the problem.

$$\frac{1}{3} + \frac{1}{6} = \frac{2}{6} + \frac{1}{6}$$

$$= \frac{3}{6}$$

$$= \frac{1}{2}$$

The total time they took to solve the problem was **$\frac{1}{2}$ h**.

Solve each of these problems. Show your work and statements clearly.

1. A sum of money was shared between Alvin and David. If Alvin got $\frac{3}{4}$ of the money, what fraction of the money did David get?

2. Aaron ate $\frac{1}{5}$ of a mango and gave the rest of it to May. What fraction of the mango did he give to May?

3. Kelvin ate $\frac{3}{8}$ of a papaya and Wendy ate $\frac{1}{8}$ of the papaya. What fraction of the papaya did they eat altogether?

4. $\frac{3}{11}$ of Sally's paper clips are red and $\frac{4}{11}$ of them are blue. What fraction of her paper clips are red and blue?

5. Paul drank $\frac{5}{12}$ of a bottle of milk. What fraction of the milk was left?

6. $\frac{5}{9}$ of a box of chocolates are round and $\frac{2}{9}$ of them are square. How many more round chocolates than square chocolates are there? Give your answer as a fraction.

7. $\frac{6}{10}$ of a class of students like soccer and $\frac{3}{10}$ of them like tennis. How many more students like soccer than tennis? Give your answer as a fraction.

8. A group of visitors visited a museum yesterday. $\frac{1}{3}$ of them were boys and $\frac{1}{9}$ of them were girls. What fraction of the visitors were children?

9. $\frac{1}{2}$ of Jerry's marbles are yellow and $\frac{5}{12}$ of them are green. What fraction of his marbles are yellow and green?

10. A box of pencils was shared among some children. Bob received $\frac{1}{4}$ of the pencils and Mark received $\frac{5}{12}$ of the pencils. What fraction of the pencils did Mark get more than Bob?

11. In an aquarium, $\frac{2}{3}$ of the fish are guppies and $\frac{1}{12}$ of them are goldfish. How many fewer goldfish than guppies are there? Give your answer as a fraction.

12. Mike drank $\frac{3}{10}$ of a pot of tea in the morning and $\frac{2}{5}$ of it in the afternoon. What fraction of the tea did he drink altogether?

13. Jane used $\frac{5}{6}$ of a piece of ribbon to tie a present and $\frac{1}{12}$ of it for the decoration. What fraction of the ribbon did she use altogether?

14. A cake was cut into 12 equal pieces. Jim ate 2 pieces and Tom ate 4 pieces. What fraction of the cake was left?

15. A watermelon was cut into 10 equal slices. Jane ate 1 slice and Terry ate 3 slices. What fraction of the watermelon was left?

Solve each of these problems. Show your work and statements clearly.

16. Tony gave $\frac{1}{5}$ of his stickers to Sam and $\frac{7}{10}$ of them to Nancy. What fraction of his stickers did he have left?

17. Mr. Benny spends $\frac{1}{4}$ of his monthly income on clothing, $\frac{1}{8}$ of it on food and saves the rest. What fraction of his income does he save each month?

18. $\frac{1}{3}$ of a group of tourists are Chinese, $\frac{2}{9}$ of them are Japanese and $\frac{1}{9}$ of them are Koreans. What fraction of the group of tourists are Chinese, Japanese and Koreans altogether?

19. A certain number of marbles was shared among John, Kevin and Jeffrey. If John got $\frac{1}{5}$ of the marbles and Kevin got $\frac{3}{10}$ of the marbles, what fraction of the marbles did Jeffrey get?

20. $\frac{1}{12}$ of Jack's stamps are from the United States, $\frac{2}{3}$ of them are from Spain and the rest are from China. What fraction of his stamps are from China?

21. Peter was given $\frac{1}{2}$ h to solve 3 puzzles. He took $\frac{1}{6}$ h to solve the first puzzle and $\frac{1}{6}$ h to solve the second puzzle. How much time did he have left for the third puzzle?

22. Jeffrey read $\frac{4}{9}$ of a book on Monday, $\frac{1}{3}$ of it on Tuesday and $\frac{1}{9}$ of it on Wednesday. What fraction of the book did he read in the three days altogether?

23. After spending $\frac{1}{12}$ of her money on a shirt and part of it on a purse, only $\frac{1}{4}$ of Mandy's money was left. What fraction of her money was spent on the purse?

24. A basket of apples was shared among some children. Pauline got $\frac{1}{2}$ of the apples, and Roy and Wendy got $\frac{1}{8}$ of the apples each. What fraction of the apples did the three children get altogether?

# TOPICAL PROBLEMS 3

# MULTIPLICATION OF FRACTIONS

## WORKED EXAMPLE 1

Mike sold $\frac{2}{7}$ of his magazines last week and the rest of them this week. If he sold 30 magazines last week, how many magazines did he sell this week?

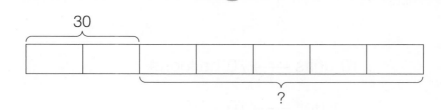

2 units $\longrightarrow$ 30 magazines

1 unit $\longrightarrow$ 30 ÷ 2

= 15 magazines

5 units $\longrightarrow$ 5 × 15

= 75 magazines

He sold **75** magazines this week.

# WORKED EXAMPLE 2

Jane has 70 balloons. $\frac{1}{10}$ of them are green and $\frac{3}{5}$ of them are orange. How many more orange balloons than green balloons does she have?

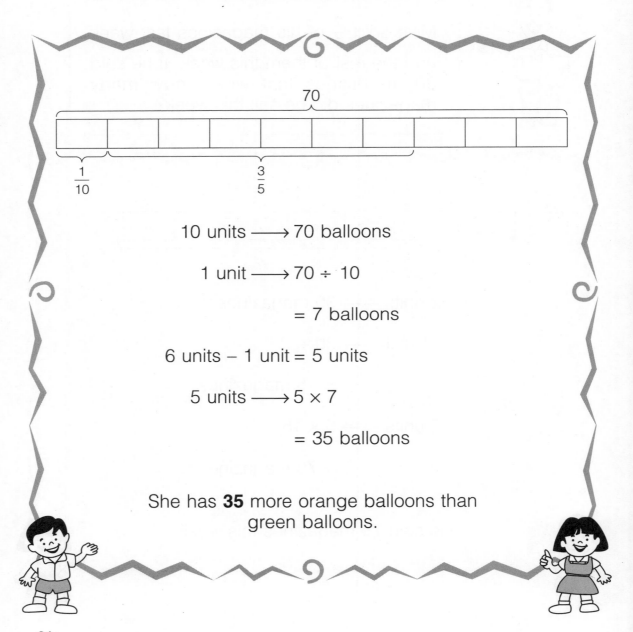

70

$\frac{1}{10}$        $\frac{3}{5}$

10 units ⟶ 70 balloons

1 unit ⟶ 70 ÷ 10

= 7 balloons

6 units − 1 unit = 5 units

5 units ⟶ 5 × 7

= 35 balloons

She has **35** more orange balloons than green balloons.

# WORKED EXAMPLE 3

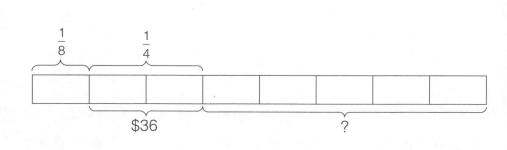

Howard spent $\frac{1}{8}$ of his money on a pair of shorts and $\frac{1}{4}$ of it on a shirt. If he spent $36 on the shirt, how much money did he have left?

$\frac{1}{8}$    $\frac{1}{4}$

$36     ?

2 units $\longrightarrow$ $36

1 unit $\longrightarrow$ 36 ÷ 2

= $18

8 units – 1 unit – 2 units = 5 units

5 units $\longrightarrow$ 5 × 18

= $90

He had **$90** left.

Solve each of these problems. Show your work and statements clearly.

1. There are 36 students in a class. $\frac{5}{9}$ of the students are boys. How many girls are there?

2. Nancy has 35 stamps. $\frac{2}{7}$ of them are from Canada and the rest are from Japan. How many stamps from Japan does she have?

3. A butcher made 100 sausages and meatballs altogether. If $\frac{3}{5}$ of them were sausages, how many sausages did he make?

4. John had 56 cookies. He ate $\frac{3}{8}$ of them. How many cookies did he have left?

5. Tom has 40 balloons. $\frac{7}{10}$ of them are blue and the rest are red. How many red balloons does he have?

6. Lynnette had 60 beads. If she lost $\frac{1}{4}$ of them, how many beads did she have left?

7. Judy bought some pens. $\frac{5}{12}$ of them were black. If she bought 60 black pens, how many pens did she buy altogether?

8. $\frac{9}{10}$ of May's coins are dimes. If she has 180 dimes, how many coins does she have altogether?

9. There were some birds at a park. $\frac{5}{8}$ of them were pigeons and the rest were crows. If there were 40 pigeons, how many crows were there?

10. A man sold $\frac{7}{12}$ of his compact discs on Monday and the rest of them on Tuesday. If he sold 84 compact discs on Monday, how many compact discs did he sell on Tuesday?

11. Wendy spent $\frac{5}{6}$ of her money and had $20 left. How much money did she spend?

12. Jackie lost $\frac{2}{9}$ of his marbles and had 126 marbles left. How many marbles did he lose?

13. Janet had $84. She spent $\frac{1}{2}$ of it on a shirt and $10 on a pair of socks. How much money did she spend altogether?

14. Lisa had 96 stickers. She used $\frac{1}{3}$ of them and gave 18 of them to her sister. How many stickers did she have left?

15. A piece of red ribbon is 10 m long. A piece of yellow ribbon is $\frac{3}{4}$ as long as the piece of red ribbon. Find the total length of the two pieces of ribbon.

## Challenging Problems

Solve each of these problems. Show your work and statements clearly.

16. Mark has 48 marbles. $\frac{5}{12}$ of them are blue and $\frac{1}{2}$ of them are yellow. How many more yellow marbles than blue marbles does he have?

17. A seamstress had 24 m of cloth. She used $\frac{7}{12}$ of it to make 5 identical shirts. How much cloth did she use to make 3 shirts?

18. A grocer had 54 lb of fish. He sold $\frac{4}{9}$ of them in the morning and $\frac{1}{3}$ of them in the afternoon. How many pounds of fish did he have left?

19. Cindy used $\frac{5}{12}$ of her money to buy a box of chocolates and $\frac{1}{4}$ of it to buy a bag of candy. If the box of chocolates cost $20, how much did the bag of candy cost?

20. Angela used $\frac{3}{10}$ of her eggs to make a cake and boiled $\frac{2}{5}$ of them. If she used 18 eggs to make the cake, how many eggs did she have left?

21. Florence read $\frac{5}{8}$ of a book on Monday and $\frac{1}{4}$ of it on Tuesday. If she read 60 pages of the book on Monday, how many more pages did she read on Monday than on Tuesday?

22. A part-time worker is paid $90 a day. He spends $\frac{1}{3}$ of the money on himself, gives $\frac{2}{9}$ of it to his mother and saves the rest. How much money does he save each day?

23. There are 40 pieces of chalk in a box. $\frac{3}{8}$ of them are red, $\frac{1}{2}$ of them are blue and the rest are white. How many pieces of white chalk are there?

24. There are 240 rabbits on a farm. $\frac{1}{4}$ of them are white, $\frac{5}{12}$ of them are grey and the rest are black. How many black rabbits are there?

# TOPICAL PROBLEMS 4

## TABLES AND GRAPHS

### WORKED EXAMPLE 1

The table below shows the prices of candy sold in bags of different sizes. Sandra bought 3 medium bags of candy and 1 large bag of candy. How much money did she pay altogether?

| Size of bag | Weight of candy | Price |
|:-----------:|:---------------:|:------:|
| Small | 100 g | $2.20 |
| Medium | 200 g | $3.90 |
| Large | 400 g | $7.30 |

3.90 + 3.90 + 3.90 = 11.70

3 medium bags of candy cost $11.70 altogether.

11.70 + 7.30 = 19.00

She paid **$19** altogether.

## WORKED EXAMPLE 2

The bar graph below shows the number of clocks that 5 shops sold last month. How many clocks did Shop A, Shop C and Shop E sell altogether?

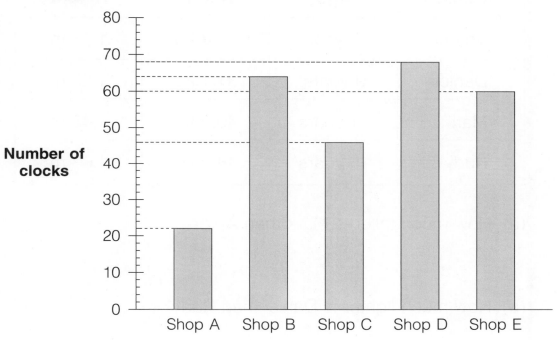

$$22 + 46 + 60 = 128$$

Shop A, Shop C and Shop E sold **128** clocks altogether.

Solve each of these problems. Show your work and statements clearly.

1. The table below shows the personal details of 4 boys.

| Name | Age | Weight | Height |
|------|------|--------|--------|
| Aaron | 10 years | 37.8 kg | 1.36 m |
| Daniel | 9 years | 31.1 kg | 1.29 m |
| Mark | 11 years | 40.2 kg | 1.42 m |
| Rudy | 15 years | 48.9 kg | 1.63 m |

(a) How much taller is Mark than Aaron?

(b) How much lighter is Daniel than Rudy?

(c) How much older is Rudy than Mark?

(d) What is the total height of Daniel and Mark?

(e) What is the total age of the 4 boys?

2. The table below shows the number of items that 4 children have.

| Name | Stamps | Coins | Stickers |
|---|---|---|---|
| Amy | 136 | 165 | 49 |
| Betty | 202 | 128 | 23 |
| Carol | 181 | 94 | 61 |
| Denise | 415 | 37 | 70 |

(a) How many more coins than stickers does Amy have?

(b) How many stamps and stickers does Denise have altogether?

(c) How many coins do Betty and Carol have altogether?

(d) How many stamps do the 4 girls have altogether?

(e) If the 4 girls share their coins equally, how many coins will each girl get?

3. The bar graph below shows the number of stamps that Jimmy has.

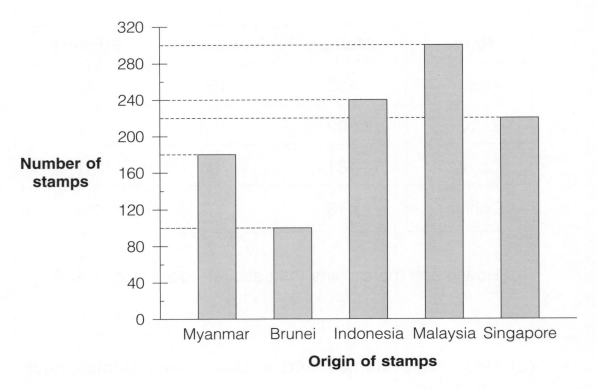

Origin of stamps

(a) How many more stamps from Indonesia than from Brunei does he have?

(b) How many stamps from Myanmar and Singapore does he have altogether?

(c) How many stamps does he have altogether?

4. The bar graph below shows the number of fruits that a fruit seller sold in a week.

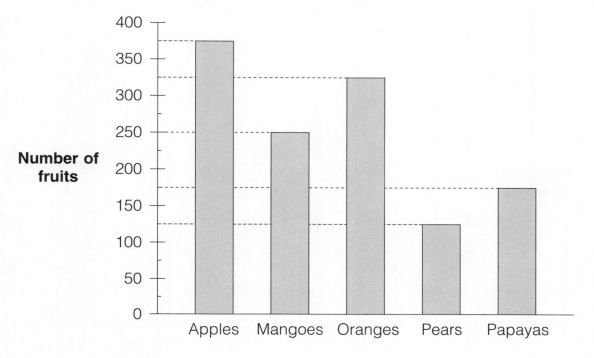

(a) If he had 610 pears at the beginning of the week, how many pears did he have left at the end of the week?

(b) How many fewer papayas did he sell than apples?

(c) How many mangoes, oranges and papayas did he sell altogether?

5. The bar graph below shows the number of marbles that 5 boys have.

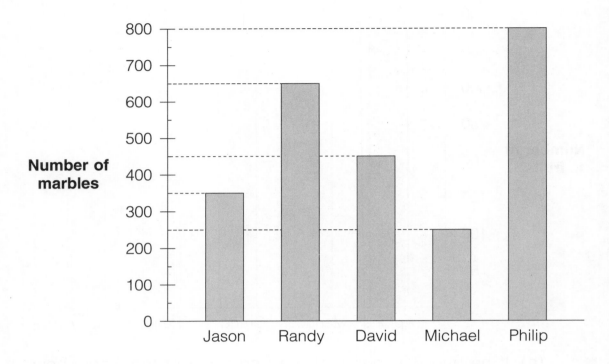

(a) How many more marbles does Randy have than Michael?

(b) How many marbles do Jason, David and Philip have altogether?

(c) If David and Philip share their marbles equally, how many marbles will each boy get?

## Challenging Problems

Solve each of these problems. Show your work and statements clearly.

6. The table below shows the number of items that a man sold in different months.

| Month | Walkman | Radios | Televisions | Cameras |
|---|---|---|---|---|
| September | 6 | 1 | 3 | 2 |
| October | 13 | 4 | 6 | 5 |
| November | 9 | 0 | 7 | 11 |
| December | 19 | 2 | 4 | 11 |

   (a) His target was to sell 5 televisions each month. In which months did he meet his target?

   (b) If each Walkman was sold at $235, how much money did he get from the sale of Walkmans in September?

   (c) In which month did he sell the most total number of Walkmans and radios?

   (d) In which month did he sell the least total number of televisions and cameras?

7. The table below shows the number of visitors to a bird park last week.

| Day | Number of local visitors | Number of foreign visitors |
|---|---|---|
| Monday | 768 | 589 |
| Tuesday | 419 | 633 |
| Wednesday | 494 | 721 |
| Thursday | 506 | 814 |
| Friday | 437 | 977 |
| Saturday | 965 | 1892 |
| Sunday | 2483 | 1674 |

(a) How many local visitors were there from Sunday to Tuesday?

(b) How many more visitors were there on Saturday than on Wednesday?

(c) 168 of the local visitors on Friday were children. How many of these local visitors were adults?

(d) There were 625 male foreign visitors on Thursday. How many female foreign visitors were there?

8. The bar graph below shows the number of televisions that a salesman sold in different months.

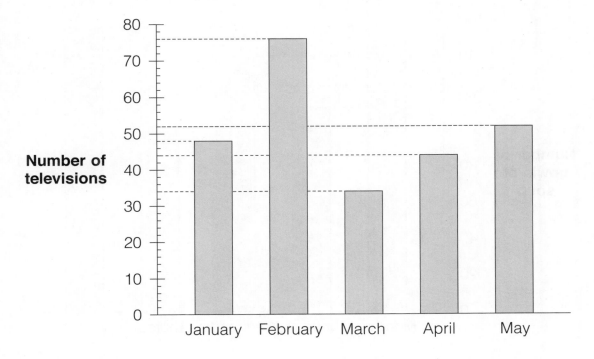

(a) How many more televisions did he sell in May than in March?

(b) If he sold each television at $448, how much money did he collect in February?

(c) For every television that he sold, the salesman received $112 commission. How much commission did he receive in April?

9. The bar graph below shows the number of bowls of soup that a restaurant sold last week.

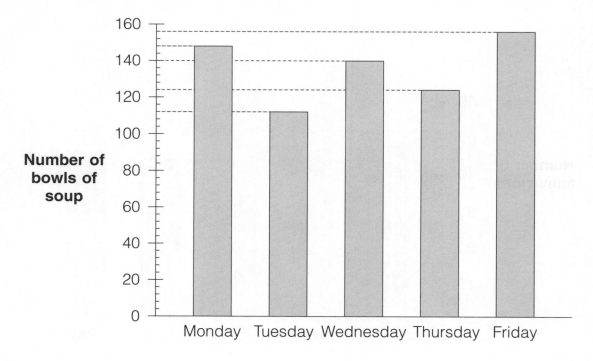

(a) How many more bowls of soup were sold on Friday than on Tuesday?

(b) The restaurant prepared 200 bowls of soup on Monday. How many bowls of soup were left at the end of that day?

(c) How many bowls of soup were sold altogether for the week?

10. The bar graph below shows the number of employees that a company employed from 1996 to 2000.

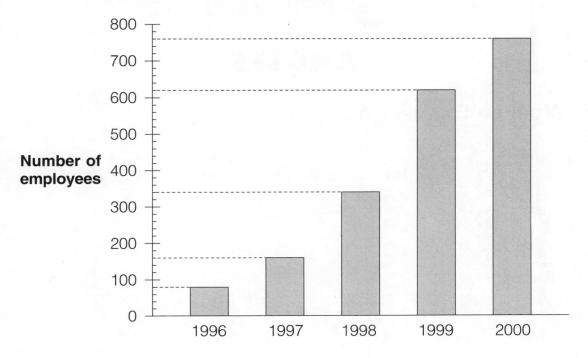

(a) What was the increase in the number of employees between 1997 and 1998?

(b) If there were 455 male employees in 1999, how many female employees were there?

(c) If 64 employees left the company in 1999, how many new employees joined the company in 2000?

# ANGLES

## WORKED EXAMPLE 1

The figure shows a rectangle *ABCD*. Find ∠*ADB*.

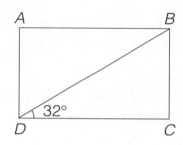

$\angle ADC \quad = 90°$

$90° - 32° = 58°$

$\angle \textbf{\textit{ADB}} \quad \textbf{= 58°}$

# WORKED EXAMPLE 2

Junior is facing the bank. If he turns through 3 right angles to his left, what will he face?

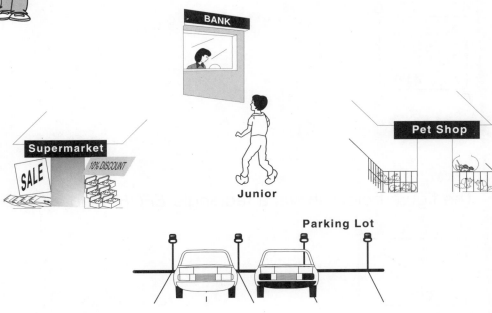

He will face the **pet shop**.

## Practice Problems

Solve each of these problems. Show your work and statements clearly.

1. The figure below shows a rectangle *ABCD*. Find ∠*BCA*.

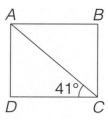

2. The figure below shows a rectangle *EFGH*. Find ∠*HGE*.

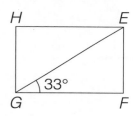

3. The figure below shows a rectangle *KLMN*. Find ∠*NMK*.

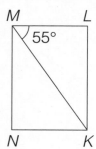

48

4. In the figure shown below, find ∠*SPR*.

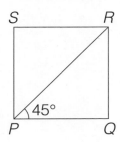

5. In the figure shown below, find ∠*TVW*.

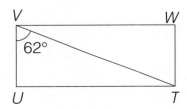

6. In the figure shown below, find ∠*WXZ*.

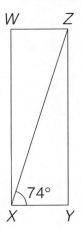

7. In the rectangle shown below, find ∠ACD.

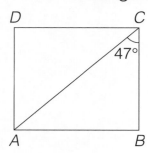

8. In the rectangle shown below, find ∠PRQ.

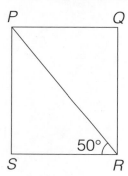

9. In the rectangle shown below, find ∠XYW.

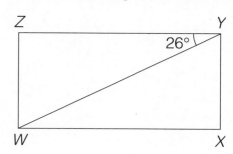

10. Use the picture to complete the table below.

Mountains

Caves

Lake

Forest

|     | Tom is facing the | If he turns through | he will face the |
| --- | --- | --- | --- |
| (a) | forest | 1 right angle to his left | |
| (b) | caves | 2 right angles | |
| (c) | lake | 3 right angles to his right | |
| (d) | mountains | 4 right angles | |
| (e) | caves | 1 right angle to his right | |
| (f) | lake | 3 right angles to his left | |

11. Use the picture to complete the table below.

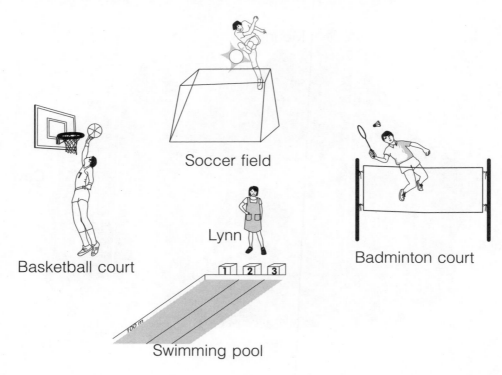

Soccer field

Basketball court

Lynn

Badminton court

Swimming pool

| | Lynn is facing the | If she turns through | she will face the |
|---|---|---|---|
| (a) | swimming pool | 2 right angles | |
| (b) | soccer field | 4 right angles | |
| (c) | badminton court | 1 right angle to her left | |
| (d) | basketball court | 2 right angles | |
| (e) | badminton court | 3 right angles to her left | |
| (f) | swimming pool | 1 right angle to her right | |

12. Use the picture to complete the table below.

Peter

Carol   Ann   Jack

Gina

|  | Ann is facing | If she turns through | she will face |
|---|---|---|---|
| (a) | Carol | 3 right angles to her right | |
| (b) | Jack | 1 right angle to her left | |
| (c) | Peter | 1 right angle to her right | |
| (d) | Gina | 2 right angles | |
| (e) | Carol | 3 right angles to her left | |
| (f) | Peter | 4 right angles | |

Solve each of these problems.

13. Draw a figure that has 8 equal angles.

14. Draw a figure that has 4 right angles.

15. Draw a figure that has 5 equal angles.

# PERPENDICULAR AND PARALLEL LINES

## WORKED EXAMPLE 1

Using a pencil, a set square and a ruler, draw a line perpendicular to the line given below.

I place my ruler against the given line and my set square against the ruler to draw a perpendicular line.

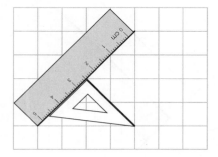

# WORKED EXAMPLE 2

Using a pencil, a set square and a ruler, draw a line parallel to the line given below.

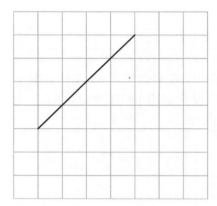

I place my ruler against the given line and my set square against the ruler. I slide the ruler along the side of the set square to draw a parallel line.

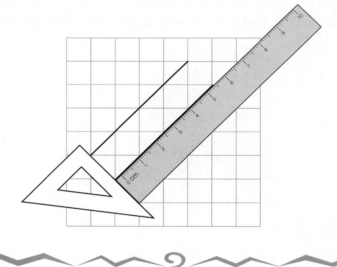

## Practice Problems

Draw a line perpendicular to each of the lines given below.

1.

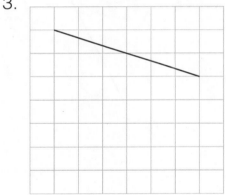

2.

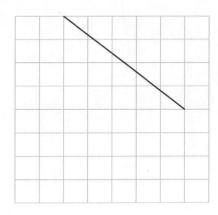

3.

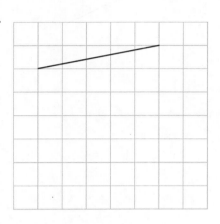

4.

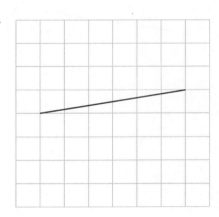

5.

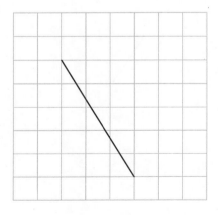

6.

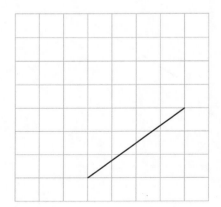

# Draw a line parallel to each of the lines given below.

7.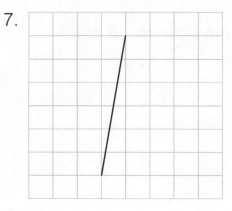

8.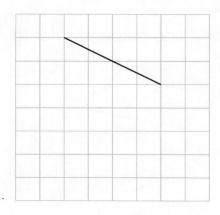

9.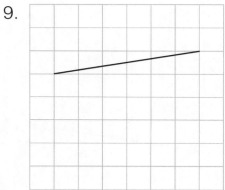

10.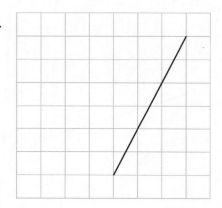

11.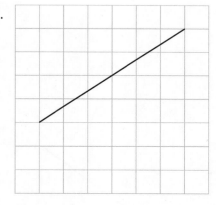

12.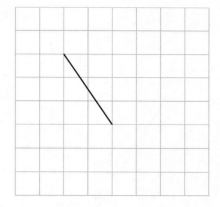

Solve each of these problems.

13. Draw a triangle that has one pair of perpendicular lines.

14. Draw a 4-sided figure that has one pair of perpendicular lines.

15. Draw a 4-sided figure that has two pairs of perpendicular lines.

16. Draw a 4-sided figure that has one pair of parallel lines.

17. Draw a 4-sided figure that has two pairs of parallel lines.

18. Draw a 4-sided figure that has two pairs of perpendicular lines and two pairs of parallel lines.

# TOPICAL PROBLEMS 7

# AREA AND PERIMETER

## WORKED EXAMPLE 1

Shape A is a rectangle that has a width of 5 cm and an area of 120 cm². Shape B is a square with an area of 81 cm². What is the difference between their perimeters?

Length of Shape A = 120 ÷ 5
= 24 cm

Perimeter of Shape A = 24 + 24 + 5 + 5
= 58 cm

Area of Shape B = 81 cm²
= 9 cm × 9 cm

Length of Shape B = 9 cm

Perimeter of Shape B = 9 × 4
= 36 cm

58 − 36 = 22

The difference between their perimeters is **22 cm**.

# WORKED EXAMPLE 2

Find the area of the figure shown.

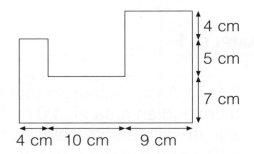

4 cm
5 cm
7 cm

4 cm    10 cm    9 cm

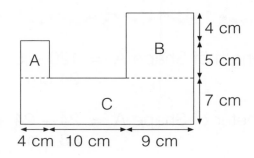

A

B

C

4 cm
5 cm
7 cm

4 cm    10 cm    9 cm

Area of A = 5 × 4 = 20 cm²

Area of B = 9 × 9 = 81 cm²

Length of C = 4 + 10 + 9 = 23 cm

Area of C = 23 × 7 = 161 cm²

Area of the figure = 20 + 81 + 161 = 262 cm²

The area of the figure shown is **262 cm²**.

## WORKED EXAMPLE 3

A rectangular plot of land measures 37 m by 22 m. It has a flower bed 1 m wide around it. Find the area of land that is covered by the flower bed.

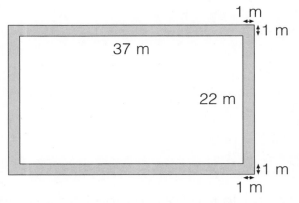

1 m

1 m

37 m

22 m

1 m

1 m

Area of inner rectangle = 37 × 22
= 814 m²

Length of outer rectangle = 1 + 37 + 1
= 39 m

Width of outer rectangle = 1 + 22 + 1
= 24 m

Area of outer rectangle = 39 × 24
= 936 m²

936 – 814 = 122

The area of land that is covered by the flower bed is **122 m²**.

Solve each of these problems. Show your work and statements clearly.

1. A rectangular painting is 9 in. wide and has an area of 288 in.$^2$. Find its perimeter.

2. A rectangular table top 92 cm long has a perimeter of 318 cm. What is its area?

3. The perimeter of a square room is 40 m. Find its area.

4.  The area of a square playground is 121 m². Find its perimeter.

5.  A rectangular farm is 10 yd wide and has an area of 850 yd². How much does it cost to fence it at $12 per yard?

6.  The perimeter of a square garden is 64 m. There is a pond with an area of 68 m² in the garden. What area of the garden is not taken up by the pond?

7. The perimeter of a rectangular hall is 144 yd and it is 18 yd wide. How much does it cost to carpet it at $43 per square yard?

8. A rectangular flower bed is three times as long as it is wide. If its perimeter is 192 ft, what is its area?

9. A cube is 14 cm long. What is its total surface area? (Hint: A cube has 6 square faces.)

10. A rectangular running track is 284 m long. It is twice as long as it is wide. If Pam ran around it three times, what was the total distance that she covered?

11. Alan ran 6 times around a rectangular field and covered a total distance of 3180 m. If the field is 76 m wide, how much longer is its length than its width?

12. The figure shows the layout of a department store. Find its area.

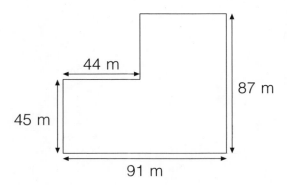

44 m

87 m

45 m

91 m

13. A farmer has a rectangular farm 82 m wide. If he spent $3312 to fence it at $9 per meter, find the area of his farm.

14. What is the perimeter of a square if its area is 64 cm²?

15. Find the perimeter of the figure shown.

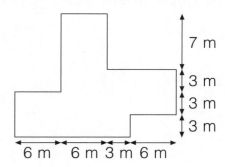

7 m

3 m

3 m

3 m

6 m    6 m 3 m 6 m

## Challenging Problems

Solve each of these problems. Show your work and statements clearly.

16. The figure shown is made up of 3 squares, each 9 in. long, placed on top of one another. Find the perimeter of the figure.

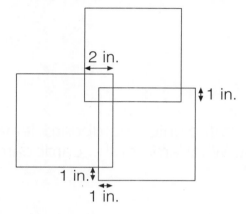

2 in.

1 in.

1 in.

1 in.

17. Richard jogged 4 times around a rectangular park. The park is 9 yd wide and has an area of 108 yd². If he had jogged around a square park 7 yd long, how many times would he have to jog around it to cover the same distance?

18. A farmer had a rectangular farm 48 m wide with a perimeter of 208 m. He divided it into 6 equal lots and used 2 of the lots to grow lettuce. What area of his farm did he use to grow lettuce?

19. The figure shown is made up of 9 equal squares, each with an area of 81 cm². If the squares are rearranged side by side in a row to form a new figure, find the perimeter of the new figure.

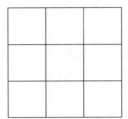

20. The figure shows a painting mounted onto a cardboard, leaving a border 8 cm wide around it. What area of the cardboard is not covered by the painting?

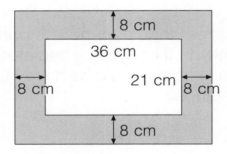

21. A square and a rectangle have the same perimeter. The square has an area of 49 cm² and the rectangle is 8 cm long. Find the area of the rectangle.

22. The figure shows the floor plan of an apartment. Find its floor area.

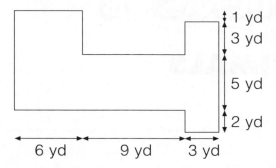

23. In the figure shown, the area of the shaded part is 95 cm². What is the perimeter of the rectangle?

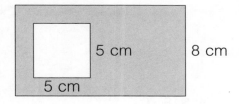

24. Steven jogged 3738 m. If he had jogged around a rectangular track 205 m long, he would have to jog around it 7 times. What was the area of the track?

# DECIMALS

## WORKED EXAMPLE 1

Gina had $18.70 less than Tracy. After Gina saved another $8.40 and Tracy spent $6.60, how much less money did Gina have than Tracy?

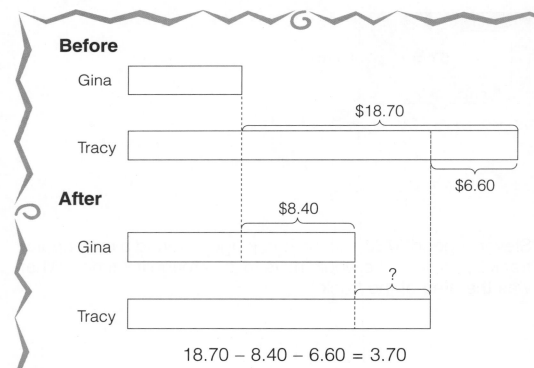

**Before**

Gina

$18.70

Tracy

$6.60

**After**

$8.40

Gina

?

Tracy

$$18.70 - 8.40 - 6.60 = 3.70$$

Gina had **$3.70** less than Tracy.

# WORKED EXAMPLE 2

String A is three times as long as String B. String C is 10.4 cm longer than String A. The total length of String A, String B and String C is 116.1 cm. How long is String C?

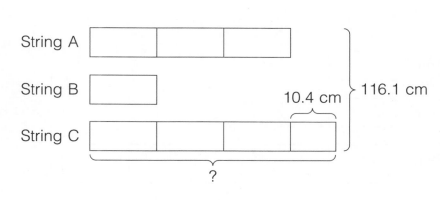

String A

String B

String C

10.4 cm

116.1 cm

?

3 units + 1 unit + 3 units = 7 units

116.1 − 10.4 = 105.7 cm

7 units ⟶ 105.7 cm

1 unit ⟶ 105.7 ÷ 7 = 15.1 cm

3 units ⟶ 3 × 15.1 = 45.3 cm

45.3 + 10.4 = 55.7

String C is **55.7 cm** long.

Ann, Carol and Pam shared $51.60. Ann received half as much money as Carol. Pam received 5 times as much money as Ann. How much money did Pam receive?

Ann

Carol

Pam

$51.60

?

1 unit + 2 units + 5 units = 8 units

8 units ⟶ $51.60

1 unit ⟶ 51.60 ÷ 8 = $6.45

5 units ⟶ 5 × 6.45 = $32.25

Pam received **$32.25**.

## Practice Problems

Solve each of these problems. Show your work and statements clearly.

1. Mavis bought 5.8 lb of rice, 2.14 lb of flour and 4.3 lb of sugar. How much more flour and sugar did she buy than rice?

2. The total height of Simon, Jack and Jerry is 4.84 m. If Simon is 1.62 m tall and Jack is 1.65 m tall, how tall is Jerry?

3. A piece of rope is 7.97 m long. A piece of string is 4.15 m longer than the piece of rope. What is the total length of the piece of rope and the piece of string?

4. Irene and Helen weigh a total of 89.07 kg. If Irene weighs 43.38 kg, how much lighter is she than Helen?

5. Jenny bought 6 bottles of 1.25 ℓ milk and a bottle of 0.8 ℓ milk. How much milk did she buy altogether?

6. A man filled his gas tank with 18.6 gal of gas. If 3 gal of gas cost $4 and he paid with two $20 bills, how much change did he get?

7. A seamstress had 34 m of cloth. She used it to make 5 identical dresses and had 13.6 m of cloth left. How much cloth did she use to make each dress?

8. Mark ran three times around a rectangular track that was 0.24 km long and 0.07 km wide. What was the total distance that he covered?

9. Fann had 10.56 m of ribbon. She cut away 7 pieces each 0.76 m long. How much ribbon did she have left?

10. 2 qt of chocolate milk cost $2.50. 3 qt of strawberry milk cost $3.90. How much more did 1 qt of strawberry milk cost than 1 qt of chocolate milk?

11. A man had 18 bags of soil each weighing 26.7 lb. He put them equally into 6 boxes. Find the weight of soil in each box.

12. A lady bought 3 ducks and 1 chicken for $38.30 altogether. The weight of the ducks were 2.7 kg, 3.1 kg and 2.4 kg. If each kilogram of duck cost $4, how much did she pay for the chicken?

13. A man is paid $54 daily if he works as a salesperson. He is paid $6.10 hourly for 12 hours of work each day if he works as a waiter. How much more money can he earn each week (7 days) if he works as a waiter than as a salesperson?

14. Ken and Paul shared $41.40 such that Ken got twice as much money as Paul. How much money did Ken get?

15. 8 toy bears cost $75.50 more than 9 toy trains. If each toy train costs $34.90, how much does each toy bear cost?

Solve each of these problems. Show your work and statements clearly.

16. Ivan had $42.30 more than Desmond. After Ivan spent $27.90 and Desmond spent $6.60, how much more money did Ivan have than Desmond?

17. Aaron has $32.95 more than James. Mike has $7.50 more than Aaron. The 3 boys have $141.20 altogether. How much money does Mike have?

18. Rope A is twice as long as Rope B. Rope C is 14.7 m shorter than Rope A. The total length of the 3 ropes is 76.8 m. How long is Rope C?

19. Jasmine, Claire and Rose shared $73.80. Jasmine received three times as much money as Claire. Rose received half as much money as Claire. How much money did Rose receive?

20. Lucas had $25.80 more than Dave. After Lucas spent $11.10, he had three times as much money as Dave. How much money did Lucas have at first?

21. Each pen cost $1.20 less than each notebook. Eric bought 8 pens and 2 notebooks. If he spent $21.90 altogether, how much did each notebook cost?

22. The total cost of 6 telephones and 1 fan is $560.90. The total cost of 1 telephone and 1 fan is $261.40. Find the cost of 1 fan.

23. 4 books and 5 magazines cost $103.60 altogether. 8 books and 3 magazines cost $134.40 altogether. How much less does each magazine cost than each book?

24. Each table costs twice as much as each chair. The total cost of 3 tables and 3 chairs is $555.30. Find the total cost of 1 table and 2 chairs.

# SYMMETRY

## WORKED EXAMPLE 1

The figure shown below is symmetrical.
Draw the line of symmetry.

I notice this figure has more than one line of symmetry. The possible lines of symmetry include the following:

The dashed line in the figure shown below is a line of symmetry. Use it to complete the figure.

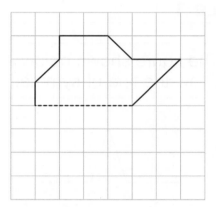

To draw the other half of the figure, I count the number of units between each point on the figure shown and the line of symmetry.

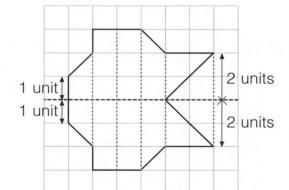

## Practice Problems

Each figure shown below is symmetrical. Draw a line of symmetry in each figure.

1.

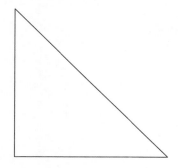

2.

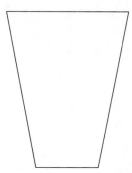

3.

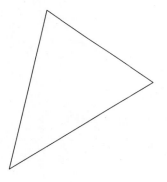

4.

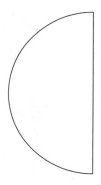

5.

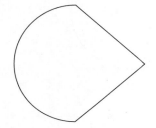

6.

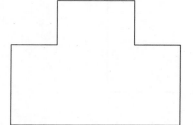

**7.**

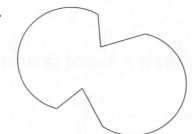

**8.**

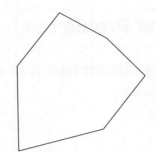

**9.**

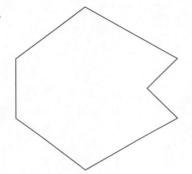

**10.**

**11.**

**12.**

## Challenging Problems

Each figure shown below is symmetrical and has more than one line of symmetry. Draw a different line of symmetry in each figure.

13.

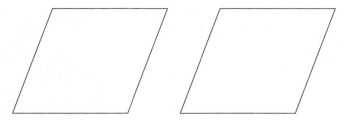

14.

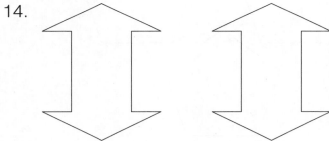

15.

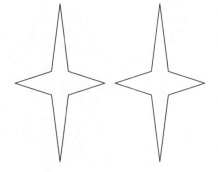

**16.**

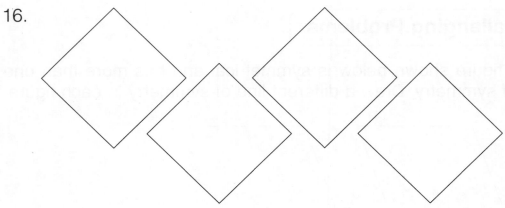

**17.**

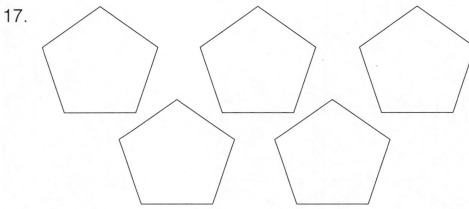

**18.**

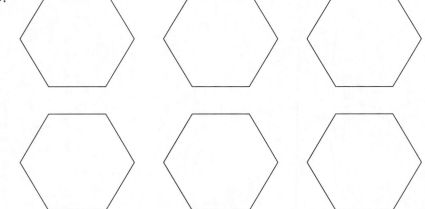

The dashed line in each figure shown below is a line of symmetry. Use it to complete each figure.

19.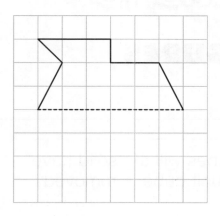

20.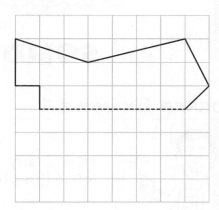

21.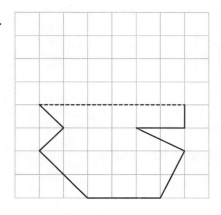

22.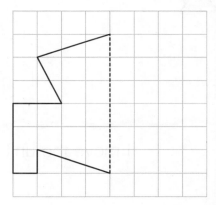

23.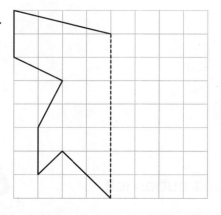

24.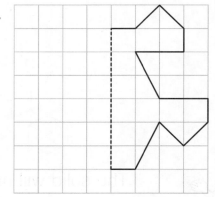

# SOLID FIGURES

## WORKED EXAMPLE 1

How many unit cubes will the solid have left if the shaded unit cube is removed?

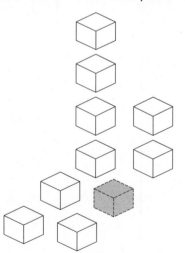

I move the unit cubes apart to count.

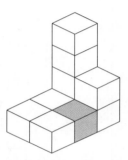

The solid will have **9** unit cubes left.

How many unit cubes will the solid have if a unit cube is added to the shaded face?

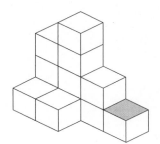

I move the unit cubes apart to count.

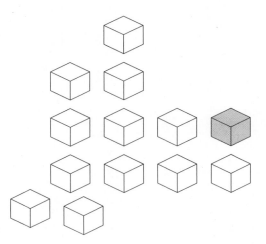

The solid will have **13** unit cubes.

## Practice Problems

Find the number of unit cubes that made up each solid below.

1.

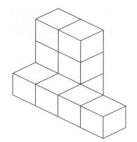

2.

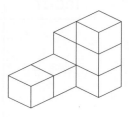

3.

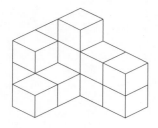

4.

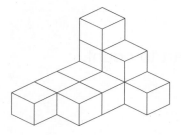

5.

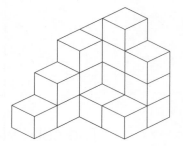

6.

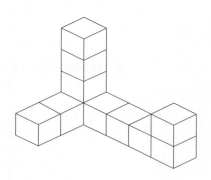

Find the number of unit cubes left in each solid when each shaded unit cube is removed.

7.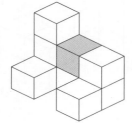

8.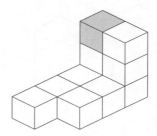

9.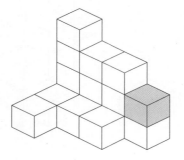

10.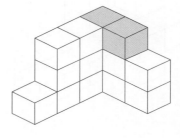

11.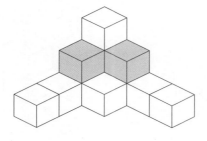

12.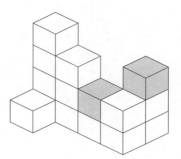

Find the number of unit cubes each solid has when a unit cube is added to each shaded face.

13.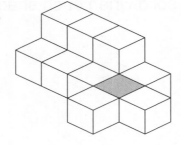

14.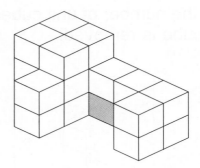

15.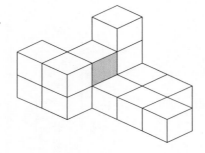

16.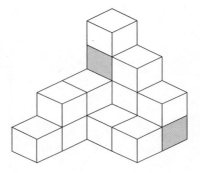

17.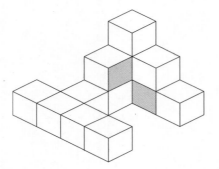

18.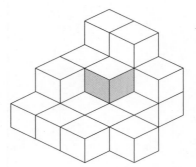

# VOLUME

## WORKED EXAMPLE 1

A 1-liter beaker contained 432 cm$^3$ of water. When 6 metal cubes were added into the beaker, 182 cm$^3$ of the water overflowed. What was the length of each metal cube? (1 $\ell$ = 1000 cm$^3$)

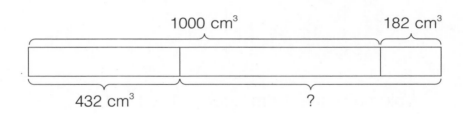

Total volume of the 6 metal cubes = 1000 + 182 − 432
= 750 cm$^3$

Volume of each metal cube = 750 ÷ 6
= 125 cm$^3$

125 = 5 × 5 × 5

The length of each metal cube was **5 cm**.

## WORKED EXAMPLE 2

A 1-cm metal cube, a 6-cm metal cube and an 8-cm metal cube were melted and recast into a new cube. Find the length of the new cube.

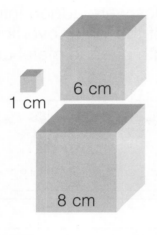

1 cm
6 cm
8 cm

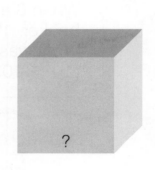

?

Volume of the 1-cm cube = $1 \times 1 \times 1$
$= 1 \text{ cm}^3$

Volume of the 6-cm cube = $6 \times 6 \times 6$
$= 216 \text{ cm}^3$

Volume of the 8-cm cube = $8 \times 8 \times 8$
$= 512 \text{ cm}^3$

Volume of the new cube = $1 + 216 + 512$
$= 729 \text{ cm}^3$

$729 = 9 \times 9 \times 9$

The length of the new cube was **9 cm**.

A rectangular container is 25 cm long, 19 cm wide and 17 cm high. Find the greatest number of 2-cm cubes that it can hold.

$$25 \div 2 = 12\frac{1}{2}$$

$$19 \div 2 = 9\frac{1}{2}$$

$$17 \div 2 = 8\frac{1}{2}$$

The greatest number of 2-cm cubes that the container can hold is 12 cubes along its length, 9 cubes along its width and 8 cubes along its height.

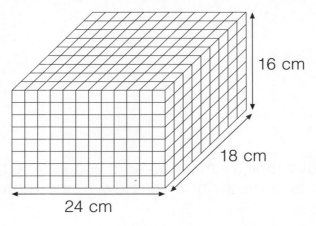

16 cm

18 cm

24 cm

$$12 \times 9 \times 8 = 864$$

The greatest number of 2-cm cubes that the container can hold is **864**.

## Practice Problems

Solve each of these problems. Show your work and statements clearly.

1. David poured 9128 cm$^3$ of water into an empty rectangular tank measuring 65 cm by 45 cm by 10 cm. How much more water could the tank hold?

2. A rectangular container 56 cm long, 42 cm wide and 16 cm high is half filled with water. How much water is there in the container?

3. A rectangular tank 17 m long, 12 m wide and 6 m high is filled with water to a depth of 5 m. How much more water can it hold?

4. A basin with a capacity of 7214 ml contained 2195 ml of water. If a cube 8 cm long is put into the basin, how much more water can it contain? Give your answer in liters and milliliters. (1 $\ell$ = 1000 cm³)

5. A solid is made up of a dozen cubes each 15 in. long. What is the volume of the solid?

6. The total volume of some water and 7 cubes, each 9 cm long, is 11,450 cm³. What is the volume of the water? Give your answer in liters and milliliters. (1 $\ell$ = 1000 cm³)

7.  A rectangular box 27 cm long, 18 cm wide and 11 cm high is filled with sand to a depth of 5 cm. If 1509 cm$^3$ of sand is poured into the box, what is the new volume of sand in the box?

8.  A man fills a rectangular container of sides 28 cm, 20 cm and 19 cm with ground meat completely. He wants to make meatballs, each of volume 10 cm$^3$, using the ground meat. Find the greatest number of meatballs that he can make.

9.  A container had 4786 cm$^3$ of sand. Lucy poured some of the sand to fill a rectangular box measuring 29 cm by 17 cm by 8 cm. Find the volume of the sand that was left in the container.

10. A rectangular tank 88 cm long, 10 cm wide and 38 cm high is $\frac{3}{4}$ filled with water. How much water is there in the tank?

11. In the figure shown, what is the volume of the water in the container?

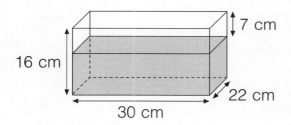

16 cm
7 cm
30 cm
22 cm

12. A rectangular container 36 cm long, 28 cm wide and 15 cm high is $\frac{3}{5}$ filled with water. How many more liters and milliliters of water can it hold? (1 $\ell$ = 1000 cm³)

13. In the figure shown, what is the volume of water needed to fill the container to its brim?

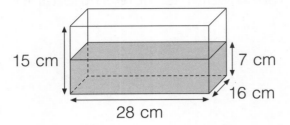

15 cm    7 cm

16 cm

28 cm

14. In the figure shown, the volume of the soil is twice the volume of the sand. Find the volume of the soil in the container.

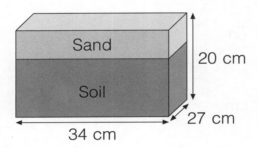

Sand

20 cm

Soil

27 cm

34 cm

15. A rectangular container measuring 32 cm by 25 cm by 12 cm was full of water. Tom poured all the water into a second rectangular container 40 cm long, 18 cm wide and 18 cm high. How much more water could the second container hold?

Solve each of these problems. Show your work and statements clearly.

16. A 1-liter beaker contained 685 cm³ of water. When 9 identical metal cubes were placed in it, 261 cm³ of the water overflowed. What was the length of each metal cube? (1 ℓ = 1000 cm³)

17. A rectangular container measuring 44 cm by 38 cm by 6 cm is half filled with water. If half of the amount of water is now poured away, how much water must be added to the container to make it full?

18. Three metal cubes were 3 cm long, 4 cm long and 5 cm long respectively. They were melted and recast into a new cube. Find the length of the new cube.

19. A rectangular container 43 cm long and 21 cm wide was filled with water to a depth of 14 cm. When 7 ℓ 21 ml of water were added into the container, 6123 cm³ of the water spilled over. Find the capacity of the container. (1 ℓ = 1000 cm³)

20. Twenty-four 4-cm cubes are needed to make a certain solid. If 2-cm cubes are used instead, how many more 2-cm cubes than 4-cm cubes will be needed?

21. A rectangular container is 24 cm long. It is half as wide as it is long and half as high as it is wide. What is its capacity?

22. The container shown below is filled with water to a depth of 12 cm. Find the volume of the water in the container.

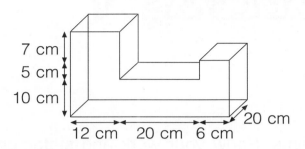

23. A rectangular container measures 21 cm by 15 cm by 23 cm. What is the greatest number of 2-cm cubes that can be put into the container?

24. The volume of Box B is $\frac{3}{5}$ the volume of Box A. The volume of Box C is 1295 cm³ more than the volume of Box B. Find the volume of Box A.

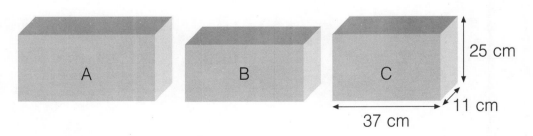

## Practice Problems

Solve each of these problems. Show your work and statements clearly.

1.  A man paid a down payment of $699 for a refrigerator. He had to pay $1\frac{1}{2}$ years' monthly installments of $46 each. How much did he pay for the refrigerator altogether?

2.  Jason and Mark have 128 action figures altogether. Paul and Jason have 176 action figures altogether. If Paul has 89 action figures, how many more action figures does Jason have than Mark?

3. Mr. Edwards estimates that he needs $7060 to go on a tour with his wife and 2 children. The cost of the tour is $2058 per adult and $1529 per child. What is the difference between the actual total cost and his estimated total cost of the tour?

4. A bucket was $\frac{5}{12}$ full of water. Mother filled another $\frac{1}{4}$ of it with water. What fraction of the bucket was filled with water?

5. A man travelled from Town X to Town Y in three days. He covered $\frac{1}{2}$ of the journey on the first day and $\frac{1}{4}$ of it on the second day. What fraction of the journey did he cover on the last day?

6. After spending $\frac{1}{6}$ of his money on a book and part of it on a shirt, Jerry had $\frac{1}{3}$ of his money left. What fraction of his money did he spend on the shirt?

7. Desmond had 64 marbles. He gave $\frac{3}{8}$ of them away. How many marbles did he have left?

8. Wendy spent $\frac{1}{6}$ of her money on a meal and $9 on taxi fare. If she had $16 left, how much money did she spend altogether?

9.  Karen spent $\frac{2}{5}$ of her money on a dress and had $138 left. How much did she pay for the dress?

10. The figure below shows a rectangle *PQRS*. Find $\angle PSQ$.

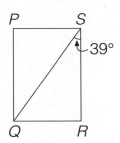

11. The figure shown has a perimeter of 64 cm. Find its area.

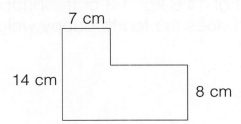

12. The area of the figure shown is 120 m². Find the length of the side *AB*.

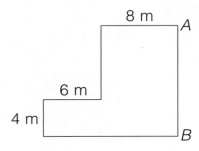

13. A rectangle is three times as long as it is wide. If it has a perimeter of 96 yd, find its area.

14. 4 puppies have a total weight of 14.8 kg. If 3 of the puppies weigh 3.6 kg each, how much does the fourth puppy weigh?

15. George had a roll of string 20 m long. He cut away 7 pieces of string each 2.46 m long. What was the length of string that he had left?

16. Marcus bought 4.32 lb of meat at $2 per lb. If he paid with a $20 bill, how much change did he get?

17. A rectangular tank 17 m long, 14 m wide and 12 m high is $\frac{1}{3}$ full of water. How much more water can it hold?

18. The table below shows the prices of 3 similar items that are sold in 4 shops.

| Shop | Electric oven | Electric cooker | Electric kettle |
|------|---------------|-----------------|-----------------|
| A | $326 | $164 | $188 |
| B | $299 | $145 | $170 |
| C | $315 | $150 | $159 |
| D | $288 | $139 | $169 |

(a) How much more does an electric oven cost at Shop A than at Shop D?

(b) How much less does an electric cooker cost at Shop B than at Shop A?

(c) A housewife bought 3 electric kettles at Shop C. How much money did she pay altogether?

(d) A man wants to buy 2 electric cookers at the cheapest price. Which shop should he buy them from?

Solve each of these problems. Show your work and statements clearly.

19. Mr. Green earns $2866 a month. He spends $488 on food and half as much on rent. He also spends $109 on transport and three times as much on others. If he saves the rest of his income, how much money does he save each month?

20. Sam had 254 stamps more than Jim on Monday. Sam gave 86 of his stamps to Jim on Tuesday. Jim gave 27 of his stamps to Sam on Wednesday. How many more stamps did Sam have than Jim in the end?

21. Cindy spent $\frac{5}{12}$ of her money on a cap, $\frac{1}{4}$ of it on a storybook and $\frac{1}{12}$ of it on a notebook. What fraction of her money did she spend altogether?

22. Jack read $\frac{3}{10}$ of a book on Monday, $\frac{2}{5}$ of it on Tuesday and the rest of it on Wednesday. What fraction of the book did he read on Wednesday?

23. After spending $\frac{1}{4}$ of his money on a book and $\frac{3}{8}$ of it on a dictionary, Jerry had $54 left. How much money did he have at first?

24. Vincent gave $\frac{2}{9}$ of his cards to Rose and $\frac{2}{3}$ of them to Andy. If Andy received 48 cards more than Rose, how many cards did Andy receive?

25. Florence had 36 chocolates. She ate $\frac{2}{9}$ of them and gave $\frac{1}{2}$ of them away. How many chocolates did she have left?

26. A square room is 12 yd long and a rectangular room is 18 yd long. The two rooms have the same perimeter. How much does it cost to carpet the rectangular room at $15 per square yard?

27. A rectangular farm is 114 m long and has a perimeter of 402 m. There is a border of trees 5 m wide around it. Find the area of land that is covered by the border of trees.

28. Angela bought 2.7 kg of fish at $8 per kg. If that was $\frac{3}{10}$ of her money, how much money did she have left?

29. If Vivian gives $2.20 to Jennifer, she will have three times as much money as Jennifer. If Vivian gives $5.80 to Jennifer, she will have twice as much money as Jennifer. How much money does Vivian have?

30. The figure shows an empty container. If it is filled with water to a depth of 11 cm, how much more water can it hold?

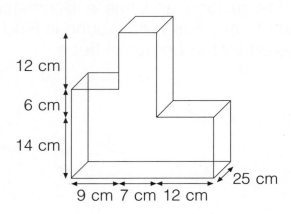

31. The bar graph below shows the number of customers who visited a restaurant last week.

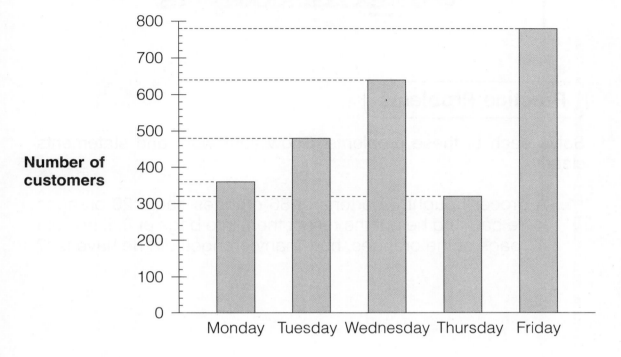

Number of customers

Monday Tuesday Wednesday Thursday Friday

(a) How many more customers visited the restaurant on Friday than on Wednesday?

(b) If each customer spent $48 on Tuesday, how much money did the restaurant receive on Tuesday?

(c) If $\frac{5}{6}$ of the customers who visited the restaurant on Monday were adults, how many of them were children?

## REVIEW PROBLEMS 2

Solve each of these problems. Show your work and statements clearly.

1.  A grocer bought 6 cartons of 86 oranges each. 20 oranges were bad and he put the rest of them into bags of 8. If he sold 47 bags of the oranges, how many oranges did he have left?

2.  There are 6 cassettes and 3 compact discs. Each cassette contains 18 songs and each compact disc contains 4 songs more than each cassette. How many songs do the compact discs and cassettes contain altogether?

3. Andrew has 38 marbles more than Roger. Leslie has 15 marbles fewer than Andrew. The 3 boys have 199 marbles altogether. How many marbles does Roger have?

4. Sandra used $\frac{3}{5}$ qt of orange juice and $\frac{3}{10}$ qt of apple juice to make some mixed fruit juice. How many quarts of mixed fruit juice did she make?

5. Margaret had a piece of ribbon $\frac{4}{5}$ m long. She cut part of it away and had $\frac{7}{10}$ m of ribbon left. How much ribbon did she cut away?

6. Jimmy took $\frac{1}{6}$ h and $\frac{1}{2}$ h to solve two puzzles respectively. How long did he take to solve the two puzzles altogether?

7. Patrick had 50 magazines. He threw away $\frac{2}{5}$ of them and bought another 15 magazines. How many magazines did he have in the end?

8. Nicholas gave $\frac{2}{7}$ of his marbles to Victor and had 20 marbles left. How many marbles did he have at first?

9. Dave has 32 stickers. Lucas has $\frac{3}{4}$ as many stickers as Dave. How many stickers do they have altogether?

10. The figure below shows a rectangle $ABCD$. Find $\angle CAD$.

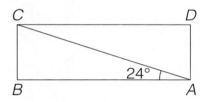

11. The area of a rectangle is 324 cm². If it is 9 cm wide, find its perimeter.

12. Find the area of the figure shown.

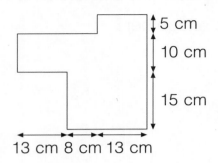

13. A square garden has an area of 144 m². How much does it cost to fence it at $28 per meter?

14. Lisa had 15.3 yd of string. She used 3.8 yd of it to tie a stack of newspapers and 2.16 yd of it to tie a pile of books. How many yards of string did she have left?

15. Calvin bought 7 pens at $2.35 each and 5 folders at $4.95 each. How much money did he spend altogether?

16. The total weight of 4 rocks is 29.54 lb. Three of the rocks weigh the same and the last rock weighs 5.15 lb. Find the weight of each of the other rocks.

17. A rectangular container measuring 36 cm by 21 cm by 15 cm is full of water. If all the water is poured into a second empty rectangular container measuring 42 cm by 20 cm by 18 cm, how much more water can the second container hold?

18. The table below shows the number of people who took part in 4 different walkathons.

| Walkathon | Boys | Girls | Men | Women |
|-----------|------|-------|-----|-------|
| A | 172 | 137 | 389 | 201 |
| B | 83 | 95 | 412 | 354 |
| C | 255 | 298 | 603 | 731 |
| D | 428 | 366 | 55 | 40 |

(a) How many fewer girls than boys took part in Walkathon A?

(b) How many more children than adults took part in Walkathon D?

(c) How many people took part in Walkathon B?

(d) How many women took part in Walkathon A, Walkathon B, Walkathon C and Walkathon D altogether?

Solve each of these problems. Show your work and statements clearly.

19. 17 cookies have 131 chocolate chips altogether. Most of them have 8 chocolate chips each but some of them have 1 chocolate chip less. How many cookies have 8 chocolate chips?

20. 8 bags and 3 caps cost $360 altogether. 4 bags and 2 caps cost $192 altogether. How much does each cap cost?

21. $\frac{3}{8}$ of a group of tourists were Japanese, $\frac{1}{4}$ of them were Americans and the rest were Chinese. What fraction of the tourists were Chinese?

22. A bag of candy was shared among some children. Aaron received $\frac{1}{12}$ of the candy, Teddy received $\frac{1}{4}$ of the candy and Pam received $\frac{5}{12}$ of the candy. What fraction of the candy did they receive altogether?

23. Alice, Ben and Tom shared 60 cookies. Alice received $\frac{1}{5}$ of the cookies, Benny received $\frac{3}{10}$ of the cookies and Tom received the rest of the cookies. How many cookies did Tom receive?

24. Mike gave $\frac{1}{8}$ of his stamps to Jane and $\frac{1}{2}$ of them to Wendy. If Mike gave 81 more stamps to Wendy than to Jane, how many stamps did he give to Jane?

25. Jackie bought 90 marbles. She gave $\frac{2}{5}$ of them to her friend and lost $\frac{1}{6}$ of them. How many marbles did she have left?

26. A square is 16 cm long and a rectangle is 4 cm wide. The area of the square is twice that of the rectangle. Find the perimeter of the rectangle.

27. A rectangular piece of paper was 32 cm long and had a perimeter of 98 cm. A square with a perimeter of 36 cm was cut away from it. What area of the paper was left?

28. 2 staplers cost as much as 3 highlighters. If 6 staplers and 6 highlighters cost $33 altogether, how much does each highlighter cost?

29. Eric has $2.55 more than Roy. Jason has 4 times as much money as Eric. The 3 boys have $24.15 altogether. How much money does Jason have?

30. A rectangular box is 45 cm long, 21 cm wide and 10 cm high. What is the greatest number of 2-cm cubes that can be put into the box?

31. The bar graph below shows the number of phone calls that a receptionist received last week.

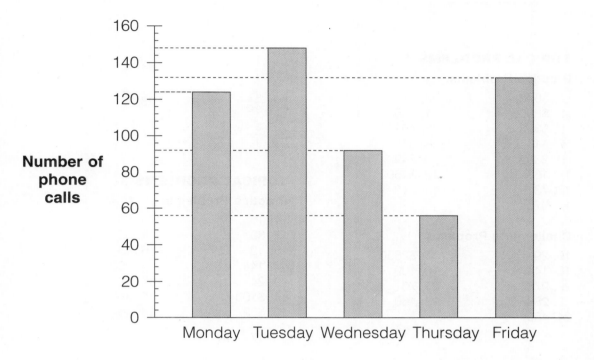

(a) How many more phone calls did she receive on Tuesday than on Thursday?

(b) If $\frac{1}{4}$ of the callers on Monday were male, how many were female callers?

(c) If $\frac{5}{6}$ of the calls on Friday were received before noon, how many calls were received after noon?

# ANSWERS

## TOPICAL PROBLEMS 1
### Practice Problems

| | |
|---|---|
| 1. $570 | 2. 77 |
| 3. $3006 | 4. 1358 |
| 5. $363 | 6. 491 |
| 7. $14,336 | 8. 67 |
| 9. 2300 g | 10. 249 |
| 11. 167 | 12. $4600 |
| 13. 731 | 14. $12 |
| 15. $70 | |

### Challenging Problems

| | |
|---|---|
| 16. 29 | 17. $2850 |
| 18. 144 | 19. 109 |
| 20. 976 | 21. 70 |
| 22. 288 | 23. 160 |
| 24. 480 | |

## TOPICAL PROBLEMS 2
### Practice Problems

| | |
|---|---|
| 1. $\frac{1}{4}$ | 2. $\frac{4}{5}$ |
| 3. $\frac{1}{2}$ | 4. $\frac{7}{11}$ |
| 5. $\frac{7}{12}$ | 6. $\frac{1}{3}$ |
| 7. $\frac{3}{10}$ | 8. $\frac{4}{9}$ |
| 9. $\frac{11}{12}$ | 10. $\frac{1}{6}$ |
| 11. $\frac{7}{12}$ | 12. $\frac{7}{10}$ |
| 13. $\frac{11}{12}$ | 14. $\frac{1}{2}$ |
| 15. $\frac{3}{5}$ | |

### Challenging Problems

| | |
|---|---|
| 16. $\frac{1}{10}$ | 17. $\frac{5}{8}$ |
| 18. $\frac{2}{3}$ | 19. $\frac{1}{2}$ |

| | |
|---|---|
| 20. $\frac{1}{4}$ | 21. $\frac{1}{6}$ h |
| 22. $\frac{8}{9}$ | 23. $\frac{2}{3}$ |
| 24. $\frac{3}{4}$ | |

## TOPICAL PROBLEMS 3
### Practice Problems

| | |
|---|---|
| 1. 16 | 2. 25 |
| 3. 60 | 4. 35 |
| 5. 12 | 6. 45 |
| 7. 144 | 8. 200 |
| 9. 24 | 10. 60 |
| 11. $100 | 12. 36 |
| 13. $52 | 14. 46 |
| 15. $17\frac{1}{2}$ m | |

### Challenging Problems

| | |
|---|---|
| 16. 4 | 17. $8\frac{2}{5}$ m |
| 18. 12 lb | 19. $12 |
| 20. 18 | 21. 36 |
| 22. $40 | 23. 5 |
| 24. 80 | |

## TOPICAL PROBLEMS 4
### Practice Problems

1. (a) 0.06 m  (b) 17.8 kg
   (c) 4 years  (d) 2.71 m
   (e) 45 years old
2. (a) 116  (b) 485
   (c) 222  (d) 934
   (e) 106
3. (a) 140  (b) 400
   (c) 1040
4. (a) 485  (b) 200
   (c) 750
5. (a) 400  (b) 1600
   (c) 625

## Challenging Problems

6. (a) October, November
   (b) $1410
   (c) December
   (d) September
7. (a) 3670     (b) 1642
   (c) 269       (d) 189
8. (a) 18        (b) $34,048
   (c) $4928
9. (a) 44        (b) 52
   (c) 680
10. (a) 180      (b) 165
   (c) 204

## TOPICAL PROBLEMS 5

### Practice Problems

1. 49°        2. 57°
3. 35°        4. 45°
5. 28°        6. 16°
7. 43°        8. 40°
9. 64°
10. (a) caves
   (b) lake
   (c) forest
   (d) mountains
   (e) forest
   (f) mountains
11. (a) soccer field
   (b) soccer field
   (c) soccer field
   (d) badminton court
   (e) swimming pool
   (f) basketball court
12. (a) Gina
   (b) Peter
   (c) Jack
   (d) Peter
   (e) Peter
   (f) Peter

### Challenging Problems

13.

regular octagon

14.

 or

     rectangle           square

15.

regular pentagon

## TOPICAL PROBLEMS 6

### Practice Problems

Accept all possible answers.
Suggested answers as follow:

1.     2.

3. 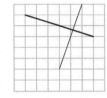    4.

5. 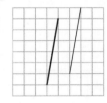    6.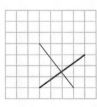

7. 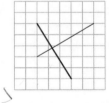    8.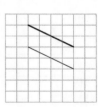

9. 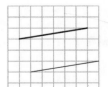    10.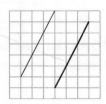

131

11. 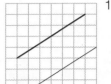  12.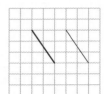

5. $2280            6. 188 m²
7. $41,796          8. 1728 ft²
9. 1176 cm²        10. 2556 m
11. 113 m          12. 6069 m²
13. 8364 m²        14. 32 cm
15. 74 m

## Challenging Problems

Accept all possible answers.
Suggested answers as follow:

13.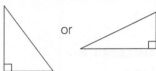

14.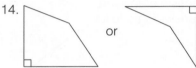

15.

16.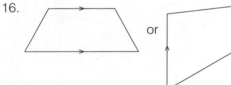

17.

18.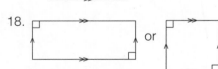

## TOPICAL PROBLEMS 7
### Practice Problems

1. 82 in.            2. 6164 cm²
3. 100 m²           4. 44 m

## Challenging Problems

16. 68 in.           17. 6
18. 896 m²           19. 180 cm
20. 1168 cm²        21. 48 cm²
22. 129 yd²         23. 46 cm
24. 12 710 m²

## TOPICAL PROBLEMS 8
### Practice Problems

1. 0.64 lb           2. 1.57 m
3. 20.09 m           4. 2.31 kg
5. 8.3 ℓ             6. $15.20
7. 4.08 m            8. 1.86 km
9. 5.24 m           10. $0.05
11. 80.1 lb         12. $5.50
13. $134.40         14. $27.60
15. $48.70

## Challenging Problems

16. $21             17. $63.05
18. 21.9 m          19. $8.20
20. $33.15          21. $3.15
22. $201.50         23. $2.50
24. $246.80

## TOPICAL PROBLEMS 9
### Practice Problems

1.            2.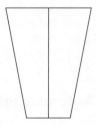

3. 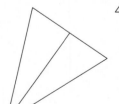           4.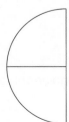

132

5.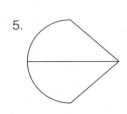

6.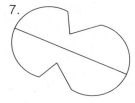

7.

8.

9.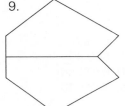

10.

11.  or

12. Accept any line through the center of the circle such as:

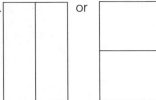

**Challenging Problems**

13.
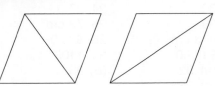

14.

15.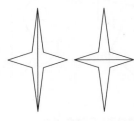

16.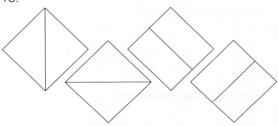

17.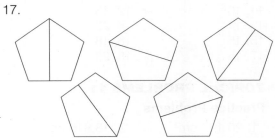

18.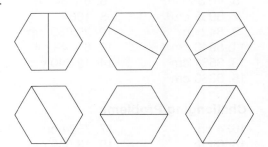

19. 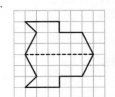     20.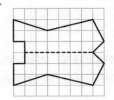

21. 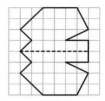    22.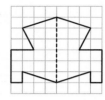

23. 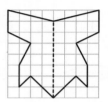    24.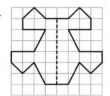

## TOPICAL PROBLEMS 10
### Practice Problems

| | |
|---|---|
| 1. 10 | 2. 7 |
| 3. 11 | 4. 11 |
| 5. 13 | 6. 18 |

### Challenging Problems

| | |
|---|---|
| 7. 8 | 8. 10 |
| 9. 15 | 10. 13 |
| 11. 10 | 12. 13 |
| 13. 14 | 14. 23 |
| 15. 15 | 16. 18 |
| 17. 15 | 18. 23 |

## TOPICAL PROBLEMS 11
### Practice Problems

| | |
|---|---|
| 1. 20,122 cm³ | 2. 18,816 cm³ |
| 3. 204 m³ | 4. 4 ℓ 507 ml |
| 5. 40,500 in.³ | 6. 6 ℓ 347 ml |
| 7. 3939 cm³ | 8. 1064 |
| 9. 842 cm³ | 10. 25,080 cm³ |
| 11. 5940 cm³ | 12. 6 ℓ 48 ml |
| 13. 3584 cm³ | 14. 12,240 cm³ |
| 15. 3360 cm³ | |

### Challenging Problems

| | |
|---|---|
| 16. 4 cm | 17. 7524 cm³ |
| 18. 6 cm | 19. 13,540 cm³ |
| 20. 168 | 21. 1728 cm³ |
| 22. 8320 cm³ | 23. 770 |
| 24. 14,800 cm³ | |

## REVIEW PROBLEMS 1
### Practice Problems

| | |
|---|---|
| 1. $1527 | 2. 46 |
| 3. $114 | 4. $\frac{2}{3}$ |
| 5. $\frac{1}{4}$ | 6. $\frac{1}{2}$ |
| 7. 40 | 8. $14 |
| 9. $92 | 10. 51° |
| 11. 186 cm² | 12. 12 m |
| 13. 432 yd² | 14. 4 kg |
| 15. 2.78 m | 16. $11.36 |
| 17. 1904 m³ | |
| 18. (a) $38 | (b) $19 |
| (c) $477 | (d) Shop D |

### Challenging Problems

| | |
|---|---|
| 19. $1698 | 20. 136 |
| 21. $\frac{3}{4}$ | 22. $\frac{3}{10}$ |
| 23. $144 | 24. 72 |
| 25. 10 | 26. $1620 |
| 27. 2110 m² | 28. $50.40 |
| 29. $34.60 | 30. 6600 cm³ |
| 31. (a) 140 | (b) $23 040 |
| (c) 60 | |

## REVIEW PROBLEMS 2
### Practice Problems

| | |
|---|---|
| 1. 120 | 2. 174 |
| 3. 46 | 4. $\frac{9}{10}$ qt |
| 5. $\frac{1}{10}$ m | 6. $\frac{2}{3}$ h |
| 7. 45 | 8. 28 |
| 9. 56 | 10. 66° |
| 11. 90 cm | 12. 720 cm² |
| 13. $1344 | 14. 9.34 yd |
| 15. $41.20 | 16. 8.13 lb |
| 17. 3780 cm³ | |
| 18. (a) 35 | (b) 699 |
| (c) 944 | (d) 1326 |

### Challenging Problems

| | |
|---|---|
| 19. 12 | 20. $24 |
| 21. $\frac{3}{8}$ | 22. $\frac{3}{4}$ |
| 23. 30 | 24. 27 |
| 25. 39 | 26. 72 cm |
| 27. 463 cm² | 28. $2.20 |
| 29. $17.80 | 30. 1100 |
| 31. (a) 92 | (b) 93 |
| (c) 22 | |